Dedicated to Esther Wolman, my great-grandmother,
whose strength and courage kept this story alive,
and to Jayna, Traci, and Deb, who helped me to tell it.
Also to Sophie, the next in the family to publish a book!

For Herb Unterman and Nancy Melton.

First Printing

COPYRIGHT @ 2009 LANDMARK HOUSE, LTD.

Unterman, Phoebe, 1992 -

International Standard Book Number: 978-0-9822874-0-8   (lib. bdg.)

Midwest Branch
Landmark House, Ltd..
1949 Foxridge Drive
Kansas City, KS   66106
913-722-0700

Southwest Branch
Kierland Corporate Center
7047 East Greenway Parkway
Scottsdale, AZ   85254
480-659-4052

Printed in China

PANEL OF JUDGES

Deborah J. Ellis
Katie Lohmann
Dr. Adolph Moser
Jayna Miller-Schneider
Jon Goodall Symon
Scot Symon
Teresa M. Melton-Symon
Nancy R. Thatch-Melton

EDITORS
Deborah J. Ellis
Nancy Thatch Melton

ASSISTANT EDITOR
Allyson Alvarez

ART DIRECTOR
Jayna Miller-Schneider

RESEARCH
Teresa M. Melton-Symon

PRODUCTION CO-ORDINATOR
Eric Taylor
Four Colour Imports

PUBLISHER
LANDMARK HOUSE, LTD.

BOOK FORMATTING
Patricia Prather
Phoebe Unterman
Rodger McReynolds

FINANCIAL SUPPORTERS
J.G. Symon & Companies

ADVISORS
Justin Benster
Arthur Malcy
Jack Mandelbaum
Norman Polsky
Robert Regnier

FOUNDER
David Melton

Creative Footprints for Kids

LANDMARK HOUSE, LTD.—Midwest
1949 Foxridge Drive Kansas City, KS 66106
913-722-0700

LANDMARK HOUSE, LTD.—Southwest
7047 East Greenway Pkwy. Scottsdale, AZ 85254
480-659-4052

Through Eva's Eyes

Written and Illustrated by
Phoebe Eloise Unterman

Based on a true story

Note to the Reader
By Eva K. Unterman

When I was the age my granddaughter Phoebe was when she started writing this story, I was readjusting to life as a teenager, living in post-war Germany with my parents. My family was Jewish, and we had been Polish citizens before the war.

Starting in late autumn of 1939, when Germany invaded Poland, the Nazis passed cruel laws against Jewish people, as they had done in all the other European countries which they occupied. We were no longer entitled to any rights and were forced to leave our home and move into a shabby, dilapidated part of the city which became known as the ghetto, where we were kept prisoner for over four years.

When she was still in elementary school, Phoebe had heard me talk about my experiences after the Nazis took over, and she had heard about our liberation after the war, but she didn't know much about how we lived before our lives changed forever; who our relatives were, what we did for fun, what kind of people my parents were. Once I told her about the lovely cottage my parents and grandparents stayed in for the summers, and how I spent time with my grandmothers, in particular, she was inspired to write about my life as a carefree child who was looking forward to going to school for the first time. This sounded to her like any normal childhood, anywhere.

Once she thought about who that little girl was, and saw a few precious photos saved throughout the war by a relative, she began to illustrate the story in her head. The opportunity arose to put the story and pictures together by entering a handmade book, written and illustrated by her, in a contest with other students of all ages. She asked questions about my life before the war, then spent a lot of time working on what she wanted to put in the story so that it would be interesting to children.

My wish is that you will learn from my story never to give up, and to look with hope toward the future. I am very fortunate and happy that Phoebe is my granddaughter, and proud of the determination and hard work she put into writing and illustrating this book.

Creative Footprints for Kids

NOTE FROM THE PUBLISHER

This book was a difficult one and a hard subject. As soon as we opened the entry of 13-year-old Phoebe Unterman, I knew that somehow and, in some way, we were meant to be its caretakers. Originally called EVA'S STORY, Phoebe wrote about the childhood memories of her Grandmother Eva in Nazi-occupied Poland during World War II. As a little Jewish girl, Eva and her family were forced by the German Nazis to live in the terrible Lodz Ghetto and then later struggled to survive one of the most notorious concentration camps—Auschwitz.

EVA'S STORY went through the same lengthy judging process as all other entries in the 10—13 Age Category of the 2006 NATIONAL KIDS-IN-PRINT CONTEST FOR STUDENTS. However, final deciding went to another worthy entry and Phoebe's book went back on a shelf to await return. Yet afterwards—every day—every week—I could not pry EVA'S STORY from my mind. It whispered to me in the dark—tugged at my conscience—and pleaded to be given a printed voice. Not being able to bear it any longer, one day I called Phoebe's mother and asked for the honor of placing Phoebe's book in our select PUBLISHER'S CHOICE GOLD AWARD LINE. Phoebe agreed.

Not only was this a harrowing tale to tell and an enormously personal one for Phoebe to write about and illustrate, it was a painful task for her to relate the entire story. The first rendition was sensitive, well-done and beautifully painted. But, it took the reader only as far as Eva and her family having to leave their nice home in Poland and go into the Lodz Ghetto. Although sad and unpleasant, it goes without saying that it was at that point when truly horrifying events began to happen all around them. It is the unspeakable that had to be spoken. If it was left unsaid, then what happened to Eva and her family—and over six million Jews—would have no more significance than a random, impersonal hurricane or earthquake. The difference between a natural catastrophe and what is now known as The Holocaust was that it was manmade—intentionally inflicted and executed upon millions of innocent men, women and children who just happened to be mainly Jewish.

In the end, Phoebe Unterman found the courage and skill to fully tell about her grandmother and renamed her book THROUGH EVA'S EYES. Miss Unterman's final paintings illuminate the pages with masterful, yet careful depictions representing one of the most tragic and brutal times in human history. This book was not just a granddaughter's tribute to her grandmother. It is furthermore an acknowledgement of those who survived and suffered the terror—and also those who died. They distantly murmur to us, "Never again. Never again."

The time is now for you to see for yourselves THROUGH EVA'S EYES.

TERESA M. MELTON-SYMON
President
Landmark House, Ltd.

The summer of 1939, rumors of war with Germany spread across Poland. Little did I know that it would be the last summer of my true childhood. I was only six years old.

Mama, Papa, and I, along with my two grandmothers, always spent our summer vacations in Zakowice, a small village outside of Łódź, the city where we lived.

We stayed in a lovely, simple little cottage. I remember going for long walks in the nearby woods, where trees grew tall, and gathering plump little berries with my Grandmother Wolman. I will never forget playing in the beautiful meadows, a place where sunflowers grew almost as tall as Papa.

During the week, Papa worked at his job in Łódź. I missed him terribly when he was away. Every weekend, I ran to the small train station to greet him as he returned from the city. I always had fun with Papa on those walks. We laughed and talked all the way back to the cottage, where Mama was waiting at the door with a smile on her face.

Everything about Zakowice was peaceful. My family was happy, and so was I. Toward the end of summer, things became different.

Papa was not his usual cheerful self. Mama seemed troubled as she went about her household duties and wore a concerned look on her face when she did her embroidering in the afternoon. I often came across my parents whispering to each other. If they saw me, they suddenly stopped. Our home became one of whispers and hushed silences. I was frightened. I wondered what was going on.

Like most children, I was curious. One night, I climbed out of my bed and hid behind the door which led to the veranda, where the adults stayed up late and played gin rummy. The soft light of the kerosene lamps revealed shadows of concern on their faces. They weren't laughing like they usually did. When they talked, their voices sounded concerned. I became uneasy when I heard them say "Germany" and "war." When Papa said, "We should return to Łódź. We should be home in case anything happens," I became scared. I had trouble falling asleep that night.

Just days later, I awoke to find Mama packing my small suitcase. "Mama, what are you doing?" I asked, wide-eyed.

"We are going home, Eva," she answered.

"But why so soon, Mama?" Before she could answer, I asked, "Does this have anything to do with all the whispering?"

She turned to me and tried to smile, but her eyes looked sad. "Don't worry about that," she tried to reassure me. "You will be fine with Papa and me." Mama realized that I had overheard far more than I should have.

We took the train back to Łódź that same day. Our vacation wasn't supposed to be over. As I sat on the train and stared out the window, I thought of Zakowice. I missed it already and I was still confused about why we left so early. However, there was something else on my mind that made me excited to return to Łódź.

I was very eager to start school in the fall for the very first time. Earlier in the summer, I'd been given a satchel for my school papers. It was made of maroon leather and my name was embossed on the front in gold letters. It was beautiful and I couldn't wait to use it.

At the height of my anticipation for the coming school year, things in Łódź were becoming very strange. I could sense that something was wrong. Mama and Papa cared much more about the bold headlines on the front page of the newspaper. They read the articles with furrowed brows and anxiety. Their secretive whispering continued. After dinner, when the adults lingered and talked, I was sent away to play alone.

Not long after, strange people poured into Łódź. They never
smiled. All of them looked so alike to me. The men were dressed in
drab green uniforms and wore armbands with a black symbol on them.
When I asked Papa what it was, he told me that it was called a
swastika.

Papa also told me that these were German soldiers. When I
passed them on the street, I couldn't take my eyes off their shiny
black boots.

One night, I couldn't fall asleep. I saw the light on in the dining room and I went to see who was still awake. Mama was sitting at the table, her sewing supplies splayed out before her. My red wool coat lay on her lap.

"Mama, what are you doing?" I asked.

"I'm sewing this yellow star to your coat," she answered. I gave her a puzzled look. "I'm sewing it to my own coat, and to Papa's, and to your grandmothers' coats, too."

"Why?" I wanted to know.

"We've been ordered by the German soldiers to wear them," she explained. "The stars show that we're Jewish." I touched the bright cotton fabric of the six-pointed star. In the center of it, there were black letters that read "Jude." I was confused. It had never mattered before that we were Jewish. Mama saw the worried look on my face. She reached over and stroked my hair.

"Don't be troubled," she said. "Just go back to bed."

Wearing yellow stars was just the beginning of what we had to do. There were many other rules we were ordered to follow. I could no longer play with my friends who weren't Jewish. I could not play in the park near our home. I couldn't even walk down my own street after dark. My biggest disappointment was not being able to go to school.

Each morning, I would stand at the window and watch longingly as the other children made their way to school. Since I wasn't allowed to go outside to see my friends, I often became very lonely.

I did, however, have my dolls. I kept my beautiful collection seated along my bedroom windowsill. I always took the very best care of them. I remember the tea parties we had on lazy afternoons that autumn. My dolls sat there politely, sipping tea and looking pretty in the beautiful dresses Mama had sewn for them.

One of the worst things the German soldiers were known for was going into Jewish homes and taking anything they wanted. One night, my whole family was seated around the table having dinner. Suddenly, the soldiers barged into our apartment. As we watched in bewilderment and terror, they took down the chandelier that hung right above our heads. Their shiny black boots were all I could look at, as the thieving soldiers balanced their feet on our dining room chairs.

The image of the shiny black boots stuck in my mind. The sounds they made when they marched down the street rang in my ears. As I lay in bed late at night, the sound of those dreadful boots played over and over in my head. I wanted it to stop! I wanted the soldiers to go away and never return. I wanted to be able to go back to Zakowice and finish our vacation. I wanted to be able to go to school. I wanted Mama and Papa, and everyone else, to be happy like they used to be. But everything just became worse.

The terrifying German occupation of Łódź brought much stress
and misery to all Jewish families. Even as a child, I realized
that we were being stripped of our rights. However, we had no
choice but to follow orders. Otherwise, men, women and children
could be in danger of being arrested or hurt by the soldiers. We
even heard of some people being transported out of town, never to
be heard from again. Mama, Papa, and my grandmothers kept careful
watch over me. They always made sure they knew exactly where I was
at all times.

Then came the cold winter day that changed my life forever. It was the day that the black boots stomped into our building. They shouted at us and ordered all Jews to leave their homes. We were not allowed to ask them where we were going, or if we were going to be able to return.

We would be leaving the next morning, so we had little time to prepare or pack. We were allowed to take only what we could carry. Mama got right to work. She made bundles from our sheets and stuffed them full of things we would need: pots and pans, silverware, a few dishes, linens, pillows, heavy down comforters, and other belongings, including a few cherished photographs. I had a little bundle of my own so I packed some paper, pencils, and my maroon leather satchel. Mama told me that I could bring only one of my dolls.

I went to my bedroom and looked at my family of dolls, trying
to decide which one I should take. It was a heartbreaking decision
for me to make. Those dolls were my playmates, my friends. I loved
all of them dearly. "I don't want to split you up," I finally told
them. "You can all stay here together. When I return, we can play
again."

I turned each one of my dolls around on the windowsill, so they
could see outside. "Now you will have something interesting to
look at," I told them. Still, I could not bring myself to choose
amongst them. I kissed them one by one and said goodbye, tears
welling in my eyes. Not willing to leave all of them, I grabbed my
beloved old rag doll, Bodwyga, and held her close.

I overheard Mama and Papa debating whether or not to take some
family treasures and keepsakes. Papa thought it would be useless
to do so. "If the soldiers find them," he said, "they will steal
them anyway."

Late that night, Papa and some other Jewish neighbors went out
to the courtyard. They buried their special heirlooms and valu-
ables there. I watched from my bedroom window and I cried as Papa
covered our belongings over with dirt.

Mama woke me very early the next morning, but I lingered in
bed, not wanting to leave my warm, comfortable home. Mama dressed
me in layers and layers of clothing because she did not know how
long we would be gone and there was not room to pack clothing. I
wore itchy woolen tights, dresses, sweaters, boots, warm gloves,
and a scarf. Of course, I also wore my red winter coat.

We joined the other Jews in our neighborhood and began our
long, cold walk into the unknown. I stayed close to Mama so that I
would not get lost in the crowd. I clutched my bundle in one hand
and Bodwyga slept safely in the crook of my other arm.

We were herded to Baluty, a part of Łódż that I had never
before seen. Mama called it the "ghetto." The place was very run-
down and looked nothing like my neighborhood. To section off the
area, the soldiers had put up high fences topped with spiraling
barbed wire. This was one of the first things about the ghetto that
frightened me. It would certainly not be the last.

We finally reached the building where we were to live. The bricks were crumbling and it looked stark and uninviting. The inside was even worse. We were all exhausted as we staggered upstairs to a dingy apartment. Its walls were bare and covered with a layer of filth. There was very little furniture and not enough beds for me, my parents, and my grandmothers.

However, Mama put aside the awful conditions and began to set up a home for our family. Her first order of business was to make up beds for all of us. She found a small sofa in the apartment and covered it with sheets and a feather-filled comforter. This bed was to be mine.

Mama may have been able to make me a comfortable bed, but she couldn't rid me of my constant hunger. Never before had I felt such a severe feeling of hunger.

That first night, my tired legs ached from walking all day, and I was freezing. It wasn't the kind of freezing that woolen stockings or one of Mama's heavy quilts could relieve. It was a freezing feeling that came from the uncertainty and danger looming in the ghetto. It existed deep down in my bones, and subsided only when I was nestled safely in bed, Bodwyga in my embrace, or when the beauty of Zakowice occupied my dreams.

Mama worked hard to help us adjust to life in the ghetto. She scrounged for furniture and found a table, which she scrubbed and covered with a clean tablecloth she'd brought from home. There was a small wood-burning stove in the room which we used for cooking and warmth. We settled as best we could into this new environment. I even went to school for a while, and then took private lessons from a young man who came to our apartment and taught me Hebrew prayers. Mama and Papa went out to work and I stayed home with my grandmothers. Grandmother Wolman always felt ill and she soon died. I missed the times when we'd pick berries and take walks together in Zakowice.

The adults kept a close watch over me. Sometimes children in our building were taken out of the ghetto. I didn't know where they were going or why. They never returned.

Once, Mama and Papa rushed me out to the courtyard when there were sirens blaring in the ghetto. Other children and I climbed down a long ladder into an old, dried-up well. A lid on the top was closed and we waited until it was safe. I was frightened and confused, but I trusted Mama and Papa and I was happy I wasn't separated from them like the children who were taken from the ghetto.

My family didn't leave the ghetto until much later. The soldiers made us walk to the nearby train station. The only train was so long that I couldn't see the end of it. It was the kind of train they usually used for animals; not like the ones we rode to Zakowice.

"Papa, are you sure this is our train?" I asked.

He grabbed my hand so we wouldn't get separated in the crowd. The train was so high up, Papa had to lift me onto it. The soldiers packed us into the cars. There were so many of us in one car that we couldn't all sit down at the same time. I was thirsty and hungry, but there wasn't anything to eat or drink. It was stuffy and the stench was unbearable. I heard people moaning, crying, and the eerie sound of the train whistle. After what seemed like hours, even days, the train stopped and we were ordered to get out quickly. "Schnell! Raus, raus!" the soldiers barked.

We had to jump out of the car into a sea of people. Some were the Nazi soldiers in their shiny black boots, this time with menacing dogs at their side. In a blur, Papa disappeared into the crowd as I held Mama's hand tight. "Auschwitz," people murmured. "We're in Auschwitz."

We were pushed into a large building with the other women. Ruthless female soldiers sat at long tables. We were ordered to undress. One soldier cut off my long braids and another shaved my head. They made us take cold showers. We all stood in shock. Most women were crying, but Mama told me not to worry, that hair always grew back.

We were given coarse, striped uniforms and hard wooden shoes. Every day was the same. We stood and were counted, then given our day's ration: some soup made of potato peels, turnips and an occasional piece of potato. We also received a piece of dark bread, which we learned to save and eat a bite at a time.

It was not long before we were loaded onto another train. We were hopeful; we thought we'd be going to a better place, that nothing could be worse than Auschwitz.

To our horror and disappointment, we arrived at another concentration camp, called Stutthof, Mama told me. It was smaller but every bit as brutal as Auschwitz.

My Grandmother Kafeman became ill and was getting worse. One evening, we were all sitting on the floor in our barracks when a few soldiers came in. They said they needed socks mended and that they'd give an extra piece of bread to whoever could help. As my grandmother raised her hand, Mama squeezed mine tight. She could tell the soldiers were up to something, but she couldn't yell out to her mother to tell her not to go. The soldiers led my grandmother and a few other women out of the barracks and we never saw her again.

We stayed at Stutthof for three months, but it seemed more like three years.

When we finally left, we rode in cattle cars to Dresden to work in a metal and munitions factory. My job was to sort bullets on a conveyor belt. I was twelve years old.

One night, Mama and I were working the night shift when we heard sirens. Everyone hurried to the basement for shelter. A bomb hit the factory and it caught fire.

When it was safe, we left the building and watched the city of Dresden burn. The bombing had been terrifying, but this was the first time we'd seen the Germans suffer, too. Even in such a bleak place, there was a glimmer of hope.

Soon we began walking. The soldiers were as brutal as ever and wouldn't let us stop for anything. It was cold, and we had little clothing. We walked along highways and through small towns. Most of the townspeople stared. One man risked his life and slipped us a piece of bread. At night, we sat close together in open stadiums to keep warm. We heard my father was walking too, and that he was incredibly weak. We tried to get a piece of bread to him.

Just when I felt like I was going to die from exhaustion, we arrived at Theresienstadt. Theresienstadt was unlike the other camps I'd been to. It was much nicer—there were beds and tables. We were there only days, when we heard gunfire and saw tanks approaching the gate.

We were liberated by Russian troops and all the Nazi soldiers disappeared.

The feeling was overwhelming. We were free and the war was over! People ran about in a frenzy and everyone was crying and hugging. We were all exhausted and weak. The Russian soldiers gave us candy. All we could think about was getting something to eat. Right away, Mama and I searched for Papa. We found him looking weak and thin, but he was alive and we were all together again, which then was all that mattered.

Epilogue

Eva's reunited family tried to contact relatives, but were unsuccessful. After deciding it was still not safe for Jews to return to Łódż, the family traveled by train and at times on foot to Germany. They decided to stay in a small town called Ludwigsburg. They appealed to the mayor, who found the family a vacated apartment. He gave them the use of a storefront, where they opened a souvenir store for the Allied soldiers. Each night, Eva and her parents sat around the dining room table making souvenirs from pencils, scraps or anything else they could find. They sold these souvenirs at the shop the next day. Many American soldiers stationed in Germany after the war visited the shop. One Jewish soldier, Herb Unterman, became friends with the family. He proposed to Eva once he returned to the states, and Eva traveled across the Atlantic to marry him.

As Eva grew into adulthood, raising two children and adjusting to life in a new country thousands of miles away from her original home, she kept her wartime experience in the back of her mind. It was always there, in the past, a terrible chapter in what was otherwise a "normal" life.

As she matured and stories similar to her own became more widespread, she saw her experience in a new light. If she could share her story, maybe it would bring attention to modern violent situations that paralleled her own. Eva felt ready to gather the strength and courage she needed to begin sharing her story. She would never have guessed that the little six-year-old girl, sitting comfortably on the porch of her family's cottage in Zakowice, would grow up and become a part of history.

In addition to passing it on to her three grandchildren, Eva's story exists to honor the millions of children whose lives were so brutally cut short by the Nazis. Some of the last images they saw were the same as those seen through Eva's eyes.

Creative Footprints for Kids

LANDMARK HOUSE, LTD.